Jenny Thomson

summersdale

NAUGHTY DARES

Copyright © Summersdale Publishers Ltd 2006
Text by Jenny Thomson
Cover Image supplied by Shutterstock

Summersdale Publishers Ltd
46 West Street
Chichester
West Sussex
PO19 1RP
UK

www.summersdale.com

Printed and bound in Great Britain

ISBN: 1-84024-531-X
ISBN: 978-1-84024-531-8

About the Author

Jenny Thomson is the author of *Naughty Games for Grown-ups* and thought it was about time that dares got naughty too. Thus *Naughty Dares* was born. She can currently be found tied naked to a lamp post after she went one step too far with her research. She hopes help will come soon…

Contents

Introduction

Naughty is defined as mischievous, indecent and wicked – and that sums up the dares contained within this saucy volume. We have the full range from the funny and flirty to the downright filthy for you to add some spice to your night in or out with your mates or partner.

Come on, undo another button and release the naughtiness inside – you know you want to...

7

DARES
Naughty

WARNING: We accept no liability whatsoever for personal injuries (someone thumps you); loss of liberty (you end up in the clink) or clothes; the end of relationships (your mates fall out with you); or any other negative effects encountered by you either during or after the carrying out of these dares.

That means you can't sue, must take full responsibility for your own naughty actions and can't use this book to defend yourself in court.

Straight to the points

Points are awarded for degrees of naughtiness.

1 point dares are for those amongst us who are shrinking violets or just warming up for the real action. They won't get you into too much trouble.

DARES

3 point dares are more *Carry On* than full on. They'll attract a giggle or two and plenty of stares. Just smile manically and you should emerge unscathed.

5 point dares are downright disgraceful, designed to shock and titillate in equal measure. Be wary where you do them and who's watching.

11

★ ★ ★ ★ ★ ★ ★ ★ ★ ★

10 point dares are likely to get you nabbed by the naughty and the real police. Be warned: you might end up wearing a less pleasurable pair of handcuffs than the fluffy ones you're used to...

Remember: for the purpose of this book you need to sin to win.

Play the game, if you dare...

Girls' night out

A night out with the girls should be an occasion to remember, even if it's through a booze-induced haze and embarrassment about what you might have got up to. Try getting up to these…

1 point dares

Find a picture of voluptuous cleavage and send it to all the men in your phone book with the message 'Hello boys'.

Come up with the naffest chat-up
lines and use them on blokes. Try
'If I said you had a lovely body
would you put it in my bed?'

Go up to men and tell them
that yours is bigger than theirs.
If they ask 'Your what?', your
friends must choose the answer.

17

Carry a blow-up man doll around with you and place him on the chair next to yours when you sit down. Take it in turns to duck under the table to make sure he's 'comfortable'.

Tell everyone within earshot
that you're not wearing any
knickers. And that the breeze
makes you feel sexy.

Make up a poem about bum cleavage. Read it out to someone who's showing bum cleavage.

See who can remove their bra
the fastest without taking off
their top. See who can put it
back on again the fastest.

3 point dares

Leave your panties as a tip for
the waiter in a posh cocktail bar.
Wink at him on your way out.

Wear pointy heels and carry a whip. When you spot a bloke you fancy, crack it and say in your most dominatrix voice, 'Down boy!'

Place an order at a takeaway and incorporate naughty words into it, with actions to demonstrate. Try asking for a big breast of chicken with some spicy balls, or a large sausage supper.

24

Make yourselves bras out of black bin liners and go out wearing rubber gloves and a condom holster.

Go into a hotel wearing
something kinky and ask
the receptionist with a sexy
European accent, 'Are there
a lot of wealthy clients here?
I'm looking for new business.'
Then wink. If they even hint that
you're a prostitute,
be very offended.

26

Phone up your local pet rescue centre and ask if anyone has handed in your Rampant Rabbit.

27

Go to KFC or a kebab shop and ask what they would recommend as an aphrodisiac.

5 point dares

Stride confidently into the gents'
toilets. Act like you're in the right
place and it's all the guys who
shouldn't be there.

DARES

Have a lovers' tiff with a complete stranger. Say things like, 'You never satisfy me, all you're interested in is your own pleasure.'

Have loud phone sex on your mobile in a quiet coffee shop. When you're asked to keep it down, hand the complainer a specially-made business card with your porn name — and the number of National Rail Enquiries, just in case.

31

Perform the Meg Ryan table-thumping orgasm scene from *When Harry Met Sally* in the snootiest wine bar in town. Get one of your friends to slap you beforehand to fake that rosy glow. Place a Barbie and Ken in a Kama Sutra position in the middle of the table.

Go up to the bar in a pub, tell the bartender you've lost your whip and ask if anyone has handed it in. The next girl who goes up has to ask for something even saucier, like her vibrator, rubber fetish gear, nipple clamps etc...

Tuck your skirt in your knickers and prance about as though nothing's wrong.

Ask every man that you meet if they 'want to see your pussy' and show them a picture of your cat. Even better: bring a stuffed cat along and ask if anyone wants to 'stroke your pussy'.

Pick a random lucky guy,
blindfold him and tell him one
of your mates isn't wearing
a bra. Get him to cop a feel
of everyone's boobs to see
whether he can spot
the bra-less wonder.

Go up to a strange fella saying
your mobile isn't working.
Hand over your vibrator
(that's humming away) and
complain that it won't let you
send pictures.

10 point dares

In the street, strip down to just a T-shirt and whip out the water pistols for an impromptu wet T-shirt competition. Ask bemused passers-by to vote for a winner.

Go into a lap dancing bar and
start dancing as unsexily as
possible whilst declaring you are
there to audition.

Get ridiculously drunk in a pub, slap your boobs down on a neighbouring table and proudly announce, 'You don't get many of these to a pound.'

Scores

You could have notched up 103 points in this section.

If you scored 0–35 points: Scores? More like snores. Where's your devilish alter ego that says to hell with convention and behaving like a prude?

41

If you notched up 36–70 points: Admit it, you've had practice. Being naughty is a way of life for you.

If you hit the big 71+ points: You naughty minx! You go girl!

Boys' night out

The beer is flowing and you've just emptied an ashtray into your mate's pocket when he wasn't looking. All that's missing are some dares to determine who's got the biggest balls…

43

1 point dares

Make signs stating things like
'Plonker', 'Big Boy', 'Tranny' and
'I'm a Laydee', and wear them
taped to your backs all night.

44

Sneak away from your mates or work colleagues in the bar and phone one of them, saying that you saw their card in a phone box and are interested in using their services.

45

Ask the sexiest waitress if she
knows where the nearest XXX
video shop is. And if she does,
what she would recommend.

Tell every girl in the bar you have a foot fetish, and ask to see her shoes. Extra points if you try them on.

Go up to a girl in a group. Hand her a lace garter and say, 'I think this is yours.'

Do an impromptu rendition of a popular song down the pub, but sing your own naughty version. For example, turn 'Danny Boy' into 'Fanny Boy'.

49

Bring a bag and fill it with assorted items of ladies' clothing, like a pair of frilly panties, a bra, stockings etc. Each guy has to put his hand in the bag and wear whatever comes out.

Naughty
DARES

Carry a back scratcher and
discreetly poke it into
naughty places.

3 point dares

Loudly make a phone call to an escort agency from a pub phone complaining that the girl you 'paid for' isn't here yet. Explain in detail what kind of girl you had requested.

Go up to a woman and say, 'I am armed with a dangerous weapon.' Add that you can't find a big enough pair of trousers to 'contain it'.

53

Naughty
DARES

Take your inflatable woman
with you on a night out and beg
every woman you meet for a
piece of clothing, saying your
girlfriend's cold.

54

Approach the hottest babe in the bar and convince her that you used to be a woman. Point to your chest and tell her you have to wear a tight corset to stop your breasts showing.

Ask women to kiss you for charity. When they ask what charity, say, 'For men who are over-endowed like me.'

Get your mate to do a crude tattoo with a felt-tip pen on your bum and then go up to a pretty girl and ask if she's got a tattoo. Say you'll show her yours if she shows you hers.

Ask girls to check out your new pants, saying that your girlfriend wants you to wear sexier ones.

5 point dares

Make a hand puppet out of a
sock, with a hole cut out in front
so your middle finger is its penis.
Sidle up to a woman and ask if
she wants to meet your friend.

Wear jeans with holes in revealing places and no pants.

Hand a beautiful woman a dog lead and collar and say, 'I'm your sex slave.' Even better: have the collar on.

Ask every woman you meet if they'd like to come to a screening of a new erotic film that's been banned in several countries.

10 point dares

★ ★ ★ ★ ★ ★ ★ ★ ★ ★

Gatecrash a hen night or ladies' night in the pub and show off those *Full Monty* moves as you strip down to your pants.

Play a game of strip pool. Miss a shot and you have to remove an item of clothing. Assume European accents and whenever it's your turn say 'breasts'.

Come out of the Gents with your zipper undone. Tell the girl you were talking to, 'Sorry about that, I was just really horny.'

Find a WPC and ask if
you can take down her
particulars. You might even
get to see her handcuffs.

Whilst watching the footy in the pub, streak if your team scores a goal.

67

Find out the name of the
bartender in your local pub and
order a raunchy stripper for them
on a busy Friday night. Enjoy.

Scores

You could have got your dirty mitts on 109 points in this section.

If you scored 0–35: Call yourself a man? More like a big girl's blouse. Or maybe you just didn't have enough beers.

69

If you scored 36–70: You're a bit of a geezer. Raise your glass and your head high. Remember to take off the ladies' panties first.

If you came in at 71+: What a top geezer. One, two, three, 'Easy, Easy, Easy!'

Couple dares

Sex up those nights in (and out) with these cheeky challenges. Two can play these fiendishly naughty dares.

1 point dares

Do the housework wearing
nothing but an apron.

When you get a telemarketing call, start jumping up and down on the bed and shouting instructions for sexual positions to each other.

Phone up Directory Enquiries
and ask for someone with a
naughty sounding name, like
Hugh Janus, Phil McCrevis or
Penny Arryde.

Start talking loudly about your premature ejaculation problem in a shop queue. Yep, even if you're a girl.

75

Swap underwear for a night out
and call each other by your porn
names. Use your first pet's name
and your mother's maiden name:
you could be 'Sparky Brown' or
'Fluffy McNulty'.

DARES

When you're sitting in a bar together, go over to a girl/ guy nearby and ask them to move because they're too sexy and it's distracting.

77

Play blind man's buff, in the buff.

3 point dares

Get his and hers T-shirts made up with naughty slogans like 'We have sex in public places' and 'Smile if you've just done it', and wear them with a satisfied smile.

Walk up to a stranger. Tell them your partner has been naughty and deserves to be spanked. Ask if they would be so kind as to take care of the matter as you offer them your hairbrush.

Naughty
DARES

Record an answer machine
message with you both
faking orgasms.

Take out a lads' magazine to read together on a train.

Draw some annotated diagrams of your favourite sexual positions on the napkins at dinner and leave them behind for the waiter.

Conceal a used looking
condom up your sleeve and
let it 'accidentally' slip out as
you return from the toilets
with your partner.

5 point dares

Get fruity in the fruit and veg
section of the supermarket.
Men, you know what to do with
that cucumber. Girls, don't forget
those coconuts and melons.

Pass a note to a stranger saying that your partner doesn't satisfy you – would they like to have a go?

Mention sex in the most inappropriate setting. For example, in the bookstore, say at the top of your voice, 'You go on top this time, I'm shagged out.'

Dance the tango naked with the
curtains open.

Rub ice cubes all over each other's nipples before going out.

Go into a sex shop and pretend to be horrified at the most innocent items on sale, like a feather boa or a pair of stockings.

Tie your partner up naked in another room, put a stocking or apple in their mouth and leave them there whilst you chat happily away to a visitor in the next room. Kinky.

91

10 point dares

Take some condoms out to
dinner, make them into little
balloons and launch them at
other diners.

92

Naughty
DARES

If someone comes to the door to
sell you something, ask them to
wait a minute and come back to
the door undressed.

93

Run once around the
garden naked.

Set up a webcam and play
doctors and nurses. Dress for
the parts.

95

Go to a dinner party amongst polite company. Guys: accidentally drop a morsel of food down your girlfriend's top, apologise profusely and then proceed to eat the food from her cleavage.

Scores

You had the chance to reach heady heights by gaining 110 points in this section, but how did you rate?

If you scored 0–35 points: Surely you can be naughtier than that? You're clearly dare virgins.

If you scored 36–70 points: Not bad, but you could do with turning that naughtiness up a notch.

If you scored 71+: Wow. Not shy, are you? Your sex life must be off the scale.

Group dares

What happens when a mixed group with a sense of adventure and absolutely no inhibitions get together? A whole lot of fun, that's what. Add some of these shameless shenanigans into the mix and you can make it a night to remember.

99

1 point dares

Every time one of your friends gets up to go to the bar or toilet, shout after them, 'That's turning me on,' and wolf-whistle.

Invent a cocktail with a naughty name like Dirty Bitch, Sexual Explosion or Legs Akimbo. Then go up to the bar and order it.

Sitting with all your mates in the pub, tap your glass and loudly announce, 'I'd like to bring this swingers meeting to order.'

Stand in the toilets and hand out condoms to everyone who enters. Tell them you are the 'safe sex police'.

Squeeze into a toilet cubicle with a couple of mates and exclaim loudly: 'There's not enough room in here for a threesome.'

Make a naughty photo album
and ask strangers if they'd like
to see it.

3 point dares

Play musical statues whilst you're waiting for your order at the takeaway, using your mobile phones for music. When the music stops, instead of freezing, snog whoever you're next to, even if it's someone of the same sex.

106

Demonstrate your oral sex technique to the group. Boys use a Creme Egg, girls use the neck of a bottle.

Slip a vibrator into a stranger's handbag as you pass, making sure it's switched on. Watch their puzzled expression as they pull it out, expecting it to be their mobile ringing.

Do a sexy walk every time you go up to the bar and flirt shamelessly, licking your lips when you order. Blokes too. If they respond, say 'That's enough,' and walk off.

Start a snogging competition
in the pub.

110

Convince one of your group that you are all going back to their place for an orgy.

In the pub, plonk yourselves down at a table of total strangers and start playing Spin the Bottle as if you know them.

5 point dares

Re-enact a famous naughty scene from a movie with one of your friends. For even more fun do a gender swap – e.g. a guy plays Demi Moore getting busy at the pottery wheel while a girl fulfils the role of Patrick Swayze in *Ghost*.

Get up and do karaoke. Pretend
you are a porn star
by doing naughty things
with the microphone.

Go up to the bar and offer to pay for your round by licking the bar staff all over.

Climb onto the table and sing 'You make me feel like a natural woman' and do a sexy dance.

In the Gents, throw a bra into the cubicle next door and ask the bloke in there for it back.

On the dance floor, dance sexily next to a member of the opposite sex. As they're getting into it, start doing the David Brent dance.

Pretend you're French and kiss
everybody you meet on each
cheek. If you're really naughty,
make it their bum cheeks.

Naughty DARES

10 point dares

★ ★ ★ ★ ★ ★ ★ ★ ★ ★

Go up to a stranger and say that you're the casting team for a blue movie production company. Tell them you think they look right for one of your upcoming roles and ask them if they'd like to do an on-the-spot audition to show they've got what it takes.

Cover your face in chocolate
paint then explain to people that
you are product-testing for Ann
Summers and want them to lick
you to see if it tastes all right.

Have a group rendition of the banned French heavy-breathing hit 'Je t'aime' in the back of a taxi. You know, the one that sounds like a couple having sex.

Naughty
DARES

Take your clothes off and
make a naked living sculpture
of the Statue of Liberty in
the town square.

Scores

How did you and the gang do? 102 points were up for grabs.

If you scored 0–35 points: You're no leader of the gang. What a puny total.

If you scored 36–70 points: Pretty hot, but you could do with sexing it up a little.

If you scored 71+: Admit it, you're in jail already aren't you, or currently being chased down the street by the fuzz?

When stealing someone's stapler just isn't funny any more, beat office tedium with these dares that are guaranteed to perplex your manager:

- After every sentence, say 'mon' in a bad Jamaican accent.
- Vacuum around your desk — for half an hour.
- Attach a sign that says FAX to the paper shredder.

The office will never be the same.

Play the game, if you dare…

Summersdale Publishers Ltd * £2.99 * ISBN 1 84024 453 4

www.summersdale.com